A Children's Story Bible

Twenty stories from the New Testament

Retold by Penny Frank

*Illustrated by John Haysom,
Tony Morris and Eric Ford*

BOK6016

Copyright © 1992 Lion Publishing
Stories from *The Lion Story Bible* © 1984, 1985, 1986, 1987 Lion Publishing
This edition published in 2002 by Lion Publishing exclusively for
Hallmark Cards, Inc.
www.hallmark.com

The moral rights of the author and illustrators
have been asserted

Published by
Lion Publishing plc
Mayfield House, 256 Banbury Road,
Oxford OX2 7DH, England
www.lion-publishing.co.uk
ISBN 0 7459 4826 X

This edition first published in 1992

Library of Congress CIP data applied for

Printed and bound in Malaysia

A Children's Story Bible

CONTENTS

BEFORE YOU BEGIN...

The stories in this book all come from the New Testament part of the Bible. The Old Testament and the New Testament are two parts of one great story—the story of God's plan to save and restore his world and all the people in it.

The Old Testament is the story of a people God chose for a special purpose. The New Testament is the story of one very special person—Jesus Christ—and his followers. It begins with the birth of a baby...

A baby
called John

The Bible tells us how God sent his Son
Jesus to show us what God is like and to tell
us how we can belong to God's family and
kingdom.

This is the story of when John the Baptist
was born. He was the cousin of Jesus. God
gave John the job of getting people ready
for Jesus. You can find the story in Luke's
Gospel, chapter 1.

There was once an old man in Israel
called Zechariah. His wife's name was
Elizabeth. Everyone knew Zechariah
because he was a priest in the temple.

Zechariah and Elizabeth often talked
together about God.

'I like the old stories of when God
spoke face to face with people like
Moses and Samuel,' said Zechariah.
'I would love to hear him speaking to
me in the temple.'

'I like the old stories of the miracles God did for Sarah and Hannah,' said Elizabeth. 'If only he would give me a baby too.'

Zechariah and Elizabeth were old. They had never had any children.

One day there was great excitement at Zechariah's home. He had been chosen out of all the priests for a special duty in the temple.

Zechariah would pray for Israel inside
the temple. Elizabeth and all the other
people would wait outside and pray.

Zechariah left all the people outside in the sunshine. He walked slowly into the cool temple.

Suddenly he saw a bright light.
Zechariah was very frightened. He was
all alone. What was happening?

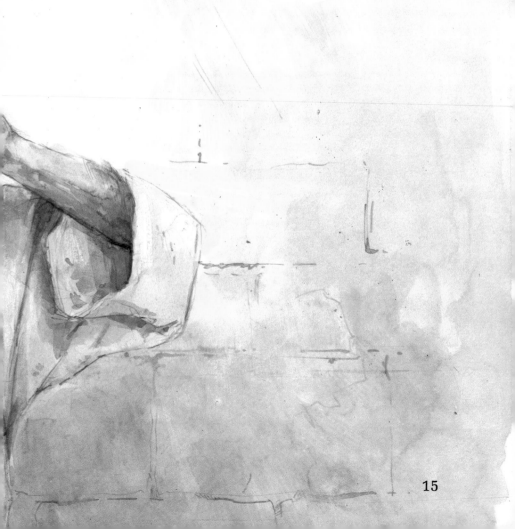

Then an angel from God spoke to
Zechariah. 'Don't be afraid, Zechariah.
God does still talk to people, and I have
come to tell you that he still does
miracles too. You and Elizabeth are
going to have a baby. You are to call
him John.

'When he grows up John will be a very special man. He will tell the people to get ready for God's Son,' said the angel.

'I must be dreaming,' said Zechariah. 'We're much too old to have a baby.'

'Don't you know how great God is?'
said the angel. 'Because you would not
believe, you will not be able to speak
until the baby is born. You'll find out
then that I have told you the truth.'

18

Elizabeth did not know why Zechariah was taking such a long time in the temple.

When at last he came out, all the people knew that something had happened, because Zechariah could not speak.

When they got home, Zechariah had to write down what had happened so that Elizabeth could understand. They were both very excited.

They started to count the weeks until the baby would be born.

While they were waiting, Elizabeth had a visit from her cousin Mary. Mary was waiting for her own baby to be born.

Mary and Elizabeth were so excited.
They had not seen each other for a
long time.

Elizabeth told Mary how the angel
had spoken to Zechariah in the temple.

Mary said to Elizabeth, 'The angel came to me too.'

They were amazed that God was sending such special babies to ordinary people.

Then Mary went back home to Joseph.

At last the day came. Elizabeth's baby was born. He really was beautiful.

All the family and friends came to see him. 'Can we cuddle baby Zechariah?' they asked.

'His name is not Zechariah,' said Elizabeth. 'His name is John. But he does love being cuddled.'

'That's silly,' the relations said. 'He should be called Zechariah. The first son is always called by his father's name.'

Then Zechariah wrote out a message for them all to read.
'HIS NAME IS JOHN,' it said.

As soon as he had written the message and obeyed what the angel of God had told him, Zechariah started to speak again.

Zechariah really enjoyed telling
everyone about what had happened.

They all looked again at the new baby.
They nodded wisely.

'That is a very special baby,' they
said. 'When he grows up John will have
special work to do for God.'

The first Christmas

Long before John was born, God had promised to send his King (the Christ) to rescue his people. But before his work could begin, they must get ready. John was sent to tell them God's King was coming, that they must change their ways and do as God wanted.

From a baby, John was special. But there was another baby, born soon after John, who was more special still. The story of this baby's birth is told in the first chapters of the Gospels of Matthew and Luke.

Long ago, before the first Christmas, there was a beautiful young woman called Mary.

She lived in the little town of Nazareth.

One day, when Mary was busy in her home, the room was suddenly full of bright light.

There, in the light, stood an angel of God. Mary was really frightened.

'Don't be afraid, Mary,' said the angel. 'The message I have for you is a message of joy. You are going to have a baby son.'

'But I have no husband,' said Mary.

'He will be the Son of God himself,' said the angel. 'You must call him Jesus.'

'I will do whatever God wants,' said Mary, and the angel went away.

There was a young man in Nazareth, called Joseph. He loved Mary. He wanted Mary to marry him.

The angel visited Joseph, in a dream.

'I have come to tell you that Mary is going to have a baby. He is the Son of God,' said the angel.

'You must call the baby, Jesus. He has come to save the whole world.'
Then the angel went away.

Mary and Joseph made their plans to get married. They loved each other very much. They often talked about the angel's message and about the special baby.

'Will people believe that Jesus is the Son of God?' said Mary.

'Don't worry,' Joseph said. 'Some people will understand. God promised he would send a special person to rescue the world. Now we can be glad that he has kept his promise.'

So Joseph and Mary waited for Jesus to be born. There were a lot of things to get ready for the baby. It seemed a long time to have to wait.

One day they heard that the Emperor
who ruled their country had made
a new law.

'Everyone must travel back to his
home town to have his name written on
a register,' Joseph told Mary. 'We will
have to go all the way to Bethlehem.'

'I would have liked to stay at home
to have my baby, but the prophets did
say that God's Son would be born in
Bethlehem,' said Mary, as the donkeys
carried them on their journey.

'I am so tired,' she said. 'And it
is such a long way.'

When they came to the town, it was very
busy. So many people had come to
register in Bethlehem that there was
no room left in the inn.

But the innkeeper said they could use
the stable where he kept his animals.

Joseph helped Mary down from the donkey and took her into the stable. Mary made a bed for them on the straw with her warm cloak. She knew her baby would soon be born.

When the baby was born, they wrapped him up warmly and made a place for him to sleep in the manger, where the animals' hay was kept.

'His name is Jesus,' they said. 'He is God's own Son.'

The animals stood watching them. Their warm breath filled the tiny stable.

It was not quiet for very long.
The stable door creaked open and some
shepherds came in.

'Where is the baby?' they asked
Joseph gently. 'Can we see him?'

'Of course,' said Joseph. 'But how did
you know a baby had been born?'

'We were out on the hills with our
sheep,' said the shepherds. 'Suddenly there
was a bright light and God's angels
came to us. They told us there was
a baby here who would grow up to save
us all. And we came at once to find
him.'

The shepherds went back to their
sheep. They told their story to everyone
they met.

Mary and Joseph stayed in Bethlehem
for a while.

One day there was a knock on the
door. Some important visitors stood
outside.

'We have come a long way to see the
baby king,' the wise men said. 'Is he
really in here?'

'Yes,' said Joseph. 'But how did
you know a baby had been born?'

'We saw a bright star in the sky,' they
said. 'Our books showed us it would lead
us to the baby born to be a king
in Israel. So we followed it.'

The visitors knelt down by the baby
and presented their gifts of gold,
frankincense and myrrh.

When the visitors had gone, Joseph and Mary looked at their baby. They had so much to think about.

They remembered the angels who had come to the shepherds, and the bright star which had led the wise men.

They looked again at the beautiful presents.

'At last God has sent his Son to Israel,' said Joseph.

'Yes,' said Mary, 'to Israel and to the whole world. Those wise men came from far away. Maybe they need him there too.'

Joseph and Mary thanked God for the baby Jesus. They knew that God had kept his promise to send his Son to save the whole world.

They did not understand yet what work God had for Jesus to do. But they knew that he would show the world what God is like.

When Jesus was young

This is the story of what happened after the baby Jesus was born in Bethlehem. The visit of the wise men is in Matthew's Gospel, chapter 2. Luke's Gospel, chapter 2 tells of Jesus in Jerusalem.

The Gospel writers do not tell us what happened in between, but it is likely that Jesus helped Joseph in the carpenter's shop, and was taught in the synagogue school like all the other boys.

Wise men from a far-off land had come
to see Jesus when he was born in
Bethlehem. They had seen a bright star
in the sky. It meant that a great new
king had been born. And so they set out
to bring him their special presents.

But the star did not lead them straight to Bethlehem. When they reached the city of Jerusalem it seemed to stop.

The wise men went at once to King
Herod's palace.

'That's where the new prince will be,'
they said.

King Herod was not pleased to hear about a new king.

'There is no baby king here,' he said. He sent for his advisers.

'The King God promised will be born in Bethlehem,' they told him.

So King Herod sent the wise men on their way.

'When you find him, come and tell me,' he said. He was a cruel man and had made a wicked plan.

The wise men found Jesus and gave him their presents, but they did not go back to King Herod. God sent them a warning.

'Don't tell the king where Jesus is,' he said. 'Go home another way.'

The king waited a long time for them.
At last he gave up and called his
soldiers.

'Go to Bethlehem,' he told them, 'and
get rid of every baby boy. I don't want
any new king growing up. Not one of
them must be left alive.'

The soldiers set off at once.

But before they reached Bethlehem, God
gave Joseph a special message.

'You must take my Son away,' he said.
'If you stay in Bethlehem King Herod
will kill him.'

So Joseph and Mary packed quickly and
took the baby Jesus to Egypt. King
Herod could not hurt him there.

They were sad to leave their own
land. They did not know how long they
would be away.

But King Herod was old and ill. After a short time, he died. God told Joseph that it was safe at last for them to take Jesus home to Nazareth. Mary and Joseph were very excited.

Their friends in Nazareth ran to meet them. It was the first time they had seen Jesus.

'What a good-looking boy Mary and Joseph have,' they said. 'How big he is.'

Joseph and Mary smiled. They were so happy to be home.

Joseph started to work as a carpenter again. He made wooden tables and benches and tools for the farmers.

The people said, 'We are glad you have come home. You are such a good carpenter. We have missed you.'

As Jesus grew up, he watched Joseph, busy in his workshop. He played with the curly wood-shavings. Soon he was learning how to use the carpenter's tools.

Once a week, on Saturday, everyone had
a rest from work. They went to the
synagogue to pray and to hear God's
Law. It was read out loud from long
scrolls.

When they were six, the boys went to
school in the synagogue on weekdays.
The teacher helped them to learn God's
Law by heart and he explained it to
them. Jesus went with the others. He
remembered his lessons well.

Soon Jesus was twelve. On his thirteenth
birthday, after a special service in the
synagogue, he and the other boys would
be treated as grown-ups.

Every year Mary and Joseph, with a
great crowd of people from Nazareth,
went to Jerusalem for the special
Passover Festival.

They walked all the way, camping out
at night. This year, for the first time,
Jesus went with Mary and Joseph.

They all had a wonderful time in Jerusalem. Each day they went to the temple to hear the teachers and to worship God. On Passover night there was a special meal. They remembered how God had rescued his people, long ago, when they were slaves in Egypt.

Jesus did not stay with Mary and Joseph all the time. He went with his friends. That was how they lost him on the way home.

When everyone camped for the night, Joseph and Mary could not find Jesus. No one had seen him all day. They would have to go back to Jerusalem to look for him.

It took them all day to get there. Next
morning, Joseph and Mary found Jesus
in the temple, talking to the teachers.
Mary was very annoyed with him.

'Didn't you know we'd be worried?'
she said.

'Surely you knew I'd be here, in my real Father's house,' Jesus answered. 'I must learn what he wants me to do.'

Then Joseph and Mary understood. Jesus knew he was God's Son. He was growing up. Soon he would have special work to do.

Jesus' special friends

As Jesus grew up, he began to discover for himself what God his Father wanted him to do.

In the next story the Bible tells us, Jesus is grown up. It is time for his work to begin. But first he meets his cousin John again...

This story comes from the first chapters of the Gospels of Mark and John.

As Jesus grew up, he often listened to people talking about his cousin, John.
He knew that John was a preacher who lived by the River Jordan.
All the people went to listen to him.

'God is sending his Son to be your king,'
John told them. 'But you are not
ready for him. You are God's special
people but you do not do as he says.'

The people knew that was true. They often broke God's laws. They found it hard to be good.

'We really are sorry,' they said. 'What shall we do?'

'Come and be baptized in the river,' said John, 'to show everyone that you really do want your life to be clean and good. And God will forgive you.'

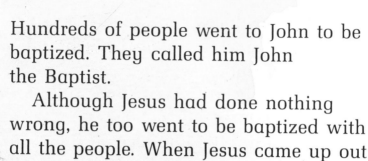

Hundreds of people went to John to be baptized. They called him John the Baptist.

Although Jesus had done nothing wrong, he too went to be baptized with all the people. When Jesus came up out of the river they heard a voice, saying:

'You are my own dear Son. I am pleased with you.'

Jesus knew that it was time to begin
God's work. It would be hard. So he
went away on his own to the desert hills
to think and pray.

He had nothing to eat for many days.

But Satan, the enemy who had spoiled
God's world, wanted to stop Jesus
from doing God's work.

He waited until Jesus was alone
and very hungry.

Then Satan tried every way he could
to make Jesus obey him, instead of God.

But Jesus said, 'I will never serve you,
Satan. God's word says I must serve
only him.'

So, in the end, Satan went away. But
Jesus knew that he would never give up.

When Jesus came back from the desert, he went home to the Lake of Galilee to begin God's work.

He saw two men fishing on the lake. 'Simon! Andrew!' Jesus called. 'Come with me! We'll go and find people for the kingdom of God, instead of fish for the market.'

Then Jesus saw two more fishermen, sitting in their boat, cleaning the nets.

'James! John!' Jesus called. 'Come on, I need you too.'

The four fishermen left everything by the lake and went with Jesus.

The next person Jesus chose to work
with him was Philip. He came from
Bethsaida, the same town as Simon
and Andrew.

Philip was very excited when Jesus
invited him to join them. He hurried
to tell Nathanael all about it.

'No one important comes from Nazareth!' said Nathanael.

But he went with Philip to meet Jesus.

'Hello, Nathanael,' said Jesus. 'I saw you sitting under that fig-tree before Philip called you!'

Jesus knew all about him! So Nathanael went with Jesus too.

One day Jesus and his special friends
were invited to a wedding, at Cana
in Galilee.

Mary, the mother of Jesus, was
helping with the wedding feast, because
she knew the bride very well.

All the guests wore their best clothes.
Everyone was very excited and happy.
The tables for the feast were bright
with flowers and the bride looked
really beautiful.

They were all enjoying themselves,
when Jesus saw Mary looking worried.
    'What is the matter?' he asked gently.

'Oh dear,' said Mary. 'This is terrible. The shame of it! People will never let us forget it. We have run out of wine. Will you help?'

Mary shook the arm of the chief servant.

'Do exactly what my son says,' she told him.

'Take those six huge jars,' Jesus said
to him, 'and fill them to the very top
with water.'

The servant did as he was told, but he
was not happy. They did not want water
to drink at a wedding.

When the jars were all full, Jesus said,
'Now pour some out and take it to the
most important guest.'

When the servant obeyed, he nearly
dropped the cup. It was full of wine!

'That's the best wine I've ever tasted,'
said the guest.

It was Jesus' first miracle, the first
of many wonderful things he did.

When Jesus went back to the Lake of Galilee, many people went with him. They had heard about the miracle at the wedding. They did not want to miss anything exciting.

They went past the place where the tax
man was sitting.

'Hey, Matthew!' called out Jesus.
'Leave all that money and come with me.
I need you.'

So Matthew got up and left
everything. He joined the group of Jesus'
special friends.

Jesus chose twelve of his followers to be his special friends. They were with him all the time. They listened when he told the people God's message. They were called the twelve apostles.

Here are their names:
Simon Peter and his brother Andrew,
James and his brother John,
Philip and Bartholomew,
Thomas and Matthew, the tax man,
another James, and Thaddaeus,
Simon the Patriot
and Judas Iscariot.

Jesus the teacher

Jesus has chosen twelve special friends. His work has begun.

Jesus loved to talk about God's kingdom and explain it to his followers. You will find some of the things he said in Matthew's Gospel, chapters 5, 6 and 7.

One day, when Jesus had gone for a walk in the hills with his friends, he said to them, 'Listen carefully. I have some really important things to tell you. You will need to remember them when I am not with you any more.'

'It's no good thinking that God's
kingdom is like this world,' said Jesus.
'If you asked the people you know what
would make them happy, they would
say being rich, or healthy, or famous.

'But I say there is happiness in God's kingdom for everyone, even those who are poor and ill and unimportant. The secret of real happiness is to love God and to do as he says.

'God wants you to pray to him. You can talk to him like this:
Our Father in heaven,
May we always show you respect.
We do want your kingdom to come on this earth, and your laws to be kept here, just as they are in heaven.
Please give us today the food that we need.
Forgive us for the wrong things we have done, and help us to forgive people who have hurt us and made us sad.
When Satan tries to make us disobey you, please help us not to do wrong.

'God is listening, even if he doesn't answer at once,' Jesus said. 'If you knock at someone's door and no one comes, you knock again. You go on knocking until the door is opened. So don't give up with God.

'Suppose you asked me for something and I didn't give it to you at once. Wouldn't you ask again? Well, prayer is like that. Don't be afraid to go on asking.

'In God's kingdom,' Jesus said, 'all the laws are good. There is a special law about loving people. Usually people like their friends and are unkind to their enemies.

'But God wants you to love even the people who hurt you. Then everyone will see that you belong to his kingdom.

'Don't always be on the lookout for things you don't like in other people. If you find fault with them they will soon turn around and point out your faults, too. In fact, don't be proud of yourself at all.

'Once upon a time a man stood in God's temple and prayed like this: "Dear God, I am so glad that I am good and keep all your laws." He was very proud.

'Another man prayed: "Dear God, please forgive me for all the wrong things I have done."

'It was that man who went home happy, for God forgave him.

'If you belong to God's kingdom, you don't have to worry about anything, ever again,' Jesus said. 'Look at those birds up there. If God makes sure they have food and drink, why should you feel worried about your next meal?

'As for new clothes — look at these
beautiful flowers, growing wild in the
field. God has given them clothes fit for
a king. He will make sure you have the
clothes you need, too.

'You want to have so many things,' Jesus said. 'And when you have them you worry about losing them. Perhaps they will get spoiled, or burglars will steal them.

'But if you belong to God's kingdom you know that the things you have don't matter very much. Your real treasure is in heaven. And there are no burglars there!

'Let's suppose there are two men, setting to work to build their new homes.

'The first one builds on solid rock. He works hard to make the foundations strong. Then he builds the walls. It takes a long time, but it's worth it.

'When the wind blows and the storms
come and the river overflows, the house
is safe. It is firm and strong on the rock.

'If you listen to me and do as I say,
you are like that man.

'The second man wants to get the job done quickly. He chooses a place where the ground is soft and sandy and easy to dig. His house is soon built.

'But when the wind blows and the storms come and the river overflows, the sandy ground is washed away. Then the house falls with a terrible crash. It can't stay there without strong foundations.

'If you listen to me but do not do as I say, you are like that man.

'I want you to be like bright lamps,'
Jesus said. 'When you light a lamp, you
don't cover it up, do you? Of course not.
You put it where it will give light to the
whole room. You are like light for the
world.

'I want you to be like a city built on top of a hill. People can see it for miles around. When they see the kind things you do, everyone will know that you belong to God's kingdom.'

Jesus gives the people food

Jesus lived in Galilee, in a country called Israel.

Because Jesus was a very special person— God's own Son—exciting things often happened to the people near him—things which showed the power of God. The people called them miracles.

This is the story of the biggest picnic ever—and how Jesus showed God's power at work.

Many people crowded to hear Jesus.
They liked to listen to what he said
about God's kingdom. And Jesus loved
to talk to them.

Some of the special friends of Jesus were fishermen on Lake Galilee. They liked taking Jesus out fishing with them.

One day they took Jesus across the lake
in their boat, to get away from the
crowds. But when they got to the other
side, they found that the people had run
around the lake to meet them.

There was a great crowd. Some of them were poor people who had no money or jobs. Others were rich and wore expensive clothes.

The children had a wonderful time.
They ran on the grass and hid behind
rocks. When they were tired they made
their way through the crowd of grown-
ups until they were close to Jesus. They
all listened to him.

'Look,' said Jesus to the grown-ups, 'to come into God's kingdom you must be like one of these little children. Then God will welcome you.'

'But what is his kingdom like?' asked the people.

'It is like a beautiful pearl,' said Jesus.
'Once you have seen it you are ready to
give all you have in order to own it.'
   'What a wonderful kingdom,'
everyone said.

By the time the evening came they were
a long way from the nearest town and
everyone was very hungry.

Jesus' friends wanted him to send the people home but Jesus said, 'No, they need some food before they go. You must give them something to eat.'

'How can we?' said his friends. 'There are so many people here.'

The friends talked together. They were
worried. There were no shops in the
hills, and anyway they had no money
to buy so much food.

A little boy who had been with them all day came up to them.

'I forgot to eat my food because I was listening to Jesus. Would you like it?'

When Jesus took the food he did not eat it himself. He told his friends to make the people sit down on the grass. They must get ready for a great big picnic.

The friends did as Jesus told them but they knew that all Jesus had was the boy's food. There were only five little rolls and two small fish.

'It's not even enough for us,' they said.

Then Jesus stood up and said thank you to God for giving them food.

Jesus picked up the boy's little basket
and said to his friends, 'You will need a
basket each to take food to all these
people.'

Jesus laughed. 'Look how far you have to carry it,' and he pointed up the hill to all the people.

Each friend had a basket. Each one took some of the rolls and fish in his basket. They obeyed Jesus.

Each friend went to a different part of the hillside. They started to give food to the people.

At first they only gave tiny pieces to
everyone.

Then they found they had enough to
give a second helping.

Soon they saw that there was plenty
of food for all the people at the picnic.

The friends stopped looking worried.
They smiled. Then they laughed. It was
just like a party.

The little boy was very pleased he
had not had time to eat his food.

When the picnic was over everyone
helped to pick up the scraps.

They put all the food which had not
been eaten into baskets. There were
twelve baskets full!

The people couldn't believe their eyes.

'It's a miracle', they said. 'Jesus had
only five rolls and two fish. Now we are
full of food and all this is left over.'

'Give thanks to God,' said Jesus. 'But God's kingdom has even better bread than this. Bread which will never go stale. Why don't you ask for that bread too?'

'What bread does God have which lasts for ever?' they asked.

'He has me,' smiled Jesus. 'I am the Bread of Life. I have come to give you life for ever.'

The story of the good Samaritan

This is a story Jesus told to show that God wants everyone in his kingdom to be ready to help others.

You can find this story in Luke's Gospel, chapter 10.

Among the people who came to hear
Jesus there were always some who tried
to make him look silly in front of the
crowds.

They thought up trick questions to ask
him because they were jealous of the
way all the people listened to him.

One day a teacher of God's Law came up to Jesus and asked a question.

'I want to have the eternal life you talk about,' he said. 'What must I do?'

Jesus answered, 'What does God's Law tell you to do?'

'It tells me to love God with all my heart
and mind, and to love other people as I
love myself.'

'That's right,' Jesus said. 'So what
don't you understand?'

The teacher had tried to trick Jesus with his question. But Jesus was too clever.

He thought quickly. 'But what does that mean?' he asked.

'Listen to this story,' said Jesus, 'and you will know the answer.'

All the crowd listened quietly while Jesus told the story.

'There was a man, all on his own, going down the dangerous road from Jerusalem to Jericho.

'Suddenly some robbers jumped out from behind the rocks at the side of the road. They beat him up and took all his money. Then they ran away.

'The road wasn't busy and it was quite a while before anyone came by.

'The first man who came was a priest. He was a bit frightened when he saw that there was a body at the side of the road.

'He was scared in case the men came back and attacked him. So he hurried by, on the other side of the road.

'The next person to come along was a Levite, who helped to look after God's temple in Jerusalem.

'He crossed the road to have a look, but he couldn't decide if the man was dead or alive. So he hurried on.'

The crowd nodded. They knew no one
could go into God's temple after
touching a dead body.

The next person coming down the road was a Samaritan.'

The crowd began to look uncomfortable. Jews hated Samaritans. What would happen next?

Jesus went on: 'The Samaritan got off his donkey when he saw the man. He took water and some soft cloth from his saddlebags.

'He saw that the man was still alive. The Samaritan cleaned the man's cuts and bruises and gave him a drink.

'When he had bandaged him up, the Samaritan lifted the man onto his donkey. He led the donkey gently down the road until they reached the inn.

'The Samaritan often stayed at that inn. The innkeeper knew him well. Soon the hurt man was safe and comfortable.

'The next day, the Samaritan had to continue his journey, but first he spoke to the man who owned the inn, and gave him some money.

"'I want you to keep on looking after
the man who was hurt," he said. "Give
him good food and let him rest here
until he is well. If it costs you more than
I have given you, I will pay when I
come back."'

Jesus turned to the clever teacher of
God's Law.

'Can you tell me which of those men
really loved the man who was hurt?' he
asked.

The teacher hated even to say the word 'Samaritan'.

'The one who took care of him,' he muttered.

'That's the right answer,' said Jesus. 'The Samaritan saw someone in need and helped him.

'That's what you must do, if you want to have eternal life and belong to God's kingdom.'

The story of the sower

This story is one which Jesus told people to help them understand God's truth. It comes in Matthew's Gospel, chapter 13.

Every day more and more people came
to find Jesus. They were excited when
they saw him heal someone and they
listened carefully to what he said. But
what they enjoyed most was when he
told them a story.

This is the story of the sower.

Once upon a time there was a farmer working on his farm. He wore tough working clothes and his face and hands were brown and wrinkled. He was used to working hard in every kind of weather.

He looked at his field. The soil was dark and crumbly. He had spent a long time getting it ready.

He walked into his field with
a large basket under one arm.
It was full of seeds.
It was good seed, the very best
he had.

As he strode up and down he took
handfuls of seed and threw it out
across the field. The good seeds went
everywhere.

There was a footpath across the farmer's field. Every day people from the village walked along the footpath to the well to get water.

The footpath was hard and flat.

When the seed fell on the path the birds could see it very easily. They swooped down and gobbled it up as it lay shining on the path. It did not get a chance to grow.

When the farmer threw the good seed across the field some fell onto ground where there were rocks. The farmer had tried to cover them with soil, but the soil was only a thin layer. Underneath, the rock was very hard.

When the seed fell there it settled into the soil and began to put down roots. But when the roots reached the rocks, they stopped growing.

There was no water in the rock, so the young plants died.

When the farmer threw the good seed across the field some of it fell at the side by the wall.

That is where the thorn bushes had been, and their seeds were still in the soil too.

So the grain and the thorn seeds grew up side by side. The grain did not have room to grow because the thorn plants were tough and strong. They took all the water and food from the soil. So the grain was choked and died.

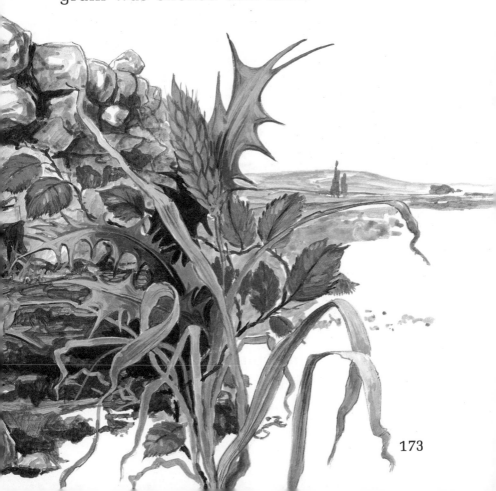

When the farmer threw the good seed
across the field some of it fell on the
good soil. It had plenty of room to
grow. Its roots could reach the water
and the sun shone down on it.

Soon the seed had roots and a green shoot.

By harvest-time there was a fat head of grain on the tall stalk. This would be cut to make flour and bread. The farmer was very pleased with the harvest.

Jesus' friends liked the story of the sower. That evening, when the crowds had gone home, the disciples sat with Jesus to eat their meal.

'What did that story mean?' they asked.

Jesus said, 'My words are like the good seed, but not everyone who hears me is like the good ground.

'When some people hear my words it is like the seeds falling on the path. Those people at once forget what I have said.

'Other people are like the rocky ground. They listen to me very carefully, but they don't give God's good seed a chance to grow.

'As for the thorn patch, people like that love to listen to me. Then they go back home to their busy lives.

'The seed has no room to grow because those people have too many other things to think about.

'But listen carefully. Some of you will be like the good ground. You hear what God is saying as you listen to me. That's the good seed.

'You want to do as God says, so God's
seed can grow. God will expect a
bumper harvest from you.

'God has given me the job of being the farmer,' said Jesus, 'and I have sown his good seed. You must decide what sort of soil your lives are going to be. God will be waiting for the harvest.'

The story of
the two brothers

This is a story Jesus told to show that God is always ready to forgive people who are sorry for disobeying him.

You can find this story in Luke's Gospel, chapter 15.

The teachers of God's Law did not like
the kind of people Jesus mixed with.

'He goes out of his way to welcome
the worst people you could think of,'
they grumbled one day.

So Jesus told them this story.

There was once a farmer who was very rich. He had two sons who worked hard for him on his farm.

The sons knew that when their father died the farm would be shared between them. They did not want their father to die, but they were looking forward to being rich.

The younger son said to his father, 'Why can't I have my share now. It's silly to have to wait for you to die before I can be rich.'

The father loved them both very much
and he wanted them to be happy. So he
shared out his farm between them.

Instead of working hard, the younger son looked at his part of the farm and said, 'What's the use of all these fields and barns? If I sell them, I'll have money to spend.'

So the younger son sold his part of the
farm and set off to seek his fortune.

The elder son stayed at home and
worked hard on his farm with his father.

The younger son went away to a big city. He had never been anywhere like that before.

There was so much food and wine.

There were comfortable inns and lots of expensive clothes to buy.

When the young men in the city saw how much money the younger son had, they were very happy to be his friends. They all enjoyed spending the money.

One morning, the younger son woke up.
After he had dressed and had his
breakfast he began to plan the day.
Everything he planned to do would cost
some money, so he looked in his
money-bag.

It was empty!

The younger son told his friends, 'We have spent all my money. What shall I do now?'

The friends just laughed and went off together. He never saw them again.

By the next day the younger son was tired and hungry.

'I shall have to find a job to earn some money,' he said.

He went to look for work on a farm, but the only job he could find was looking after the pigs.

He didn't earn much — not even enough to buy his food. He could have eaten the pig food, he felt so hungry.

Then suddenly one day, as he fed the pigs, he said to himself, 'I must be crazy. On my father's farm even the servants have more than enough to eat

'I know what I'll do. I'll go back home and I'll tell my dad that I'm really sorry for what I've done. I'll ask if I can work for him as a servant. I'm not fit to be his son any more.'

Every day, from the day his younger son had left, the father had looked down the winding road towards the city, hoping he would come back.

When at last he saw his son coming, he ran down the road to welcome him. He threw his arms around him.

'We'll have a party to celebrate,' the father said, and called the servants to bring clean clothes and a gold ring.

The older son had been working late in the fields. He heard the music and he asked the servants what the party was for.

'It's for your brother,' they said. 'Your father thought he was lost. He was afraid he was dead. But he's come back safe and sound.'

The older brother stood outside the
house and sulked.

'That's not fair,' he said. 'He should be
punished for wasting all that money, not
rewarded with a party.'

The father came out and put his arm around his older son.

'You know I love you. I don't know what I would have done without you. But your brother has come back alive. Of course I must celebrate.'

Jesus said to the teachers of God's Law, 'Do you understand? God loves you. He is glad that you do as he says and live to please him. But he is full of joy when one of his disobedient sons comes back to the kingdom.'

The story of the lost sheep

Jesus told this story to show people that they were all like lost sheep until they came into God's kingdom.

You can find it in Luke's Gospel, chapter 15.

One day, Jesus heard the teachers and
religious rulers grumbling.

'Jesus spends all his time with people
who are no good. Doesn't he know that
we are more important?'

Jesus looked at their proud faces and fine clothes. They did not listen carefully to what he said. They just tried to argue with him.

Then Jesus looked at the people sitting near him. Some were tired and hungry. Some had ragged clothes. No one else thought they were important. But they followed Jesus from town to town. They listened carefully to every word he said.

So Jesus said to the teachers and rulers, 'Listen to this story and try to understand.'

There was once a shepherd who kept his sheep up on the hills near the Lake of Galilee. He had been a shepherd all his life. He knew all there was to know about sheep.

The shepherd worked hard and his flock grew until he had one hundred healthy sheep.

He knew them all so well that he always noticed if one was limping, or had hurt itself.

One morning he was very worried. There was one sheep missing.

At first he thought he might have made a mistake. He counted again, very carefully, but sure enough there were only ninety-nine sheep in the fold.

'Now then,' said Jesus to the rulers.
'Do you think that shepherd said, "Oh,
never mind. That's too bad. At least
I still have ninety-nine"?

'Of course not! He left the ninety-
nine sheep in the sheepfold and set out
at once to look for the one that was
lost.'

That man was a good shepherd. He knew exactly which one of the sheep had wandered away. He would not rest until he found it.

The shepherd knew the hillsides very well. He knew all the places where a sheep might stray. He knew all the dangerous places where a sheep might fall.

The shepherd looked everywhere, even in places where he himself might get hurt. He must find his lost sheep.

At last the shepherd found his sheep, up there on the hills.

He gently pulled it out from between the rocks where it had been stuck. He bandaged up the leg which had been hurt.

Then the shepherd lifted the sheep up onto his shoulders. It snuggled around his neck and felt safe again.

The shepherd carefully made his way
back. It was getting dark now, and he
was hungry. He had been so busy
looking for his lost sheep all day that he
had not had time to eat.

The shepherd's feet were sore and bruised from the rocks on the hillside. But he did not mind. He was so pleased he had found his sheep.

He put the poor, lost sheep in the fold with the rest, and he counted them all carefully.

'Ninety-seven, ninety-eight, ninety-nine, one hundred!'

When he was sure they were all safe,
he made his way home.

As he walked along the dark street
he looked in at the doorways.

'I've found my sheep,' he called to
all his friends. 'Come and celebrate,
because I've found my sheep that was
lost.'

His friends and their families were very
pleased. They knew how important it
was to find that sheep. They all came to
celebrate with him.

'Can you understand?' Jesus asked the teachers and rulers. 'God's kingdom is like that flock of sheep. I am the good shepherd.

'There may be ninety-nine of you safely in the sheepfold, but I must search for the one who is lost.

'Even the angels in heaven celebrate when I find one of my sheep that was lost.

'I'm not like a part-time shepherd,
who is paid to look after another man's
sheep. That man doesn't really care if
the sheep are safe, because they don't
belong to him.

'I care about every one of my sheep.
I know them all by name. I always take
care of them. If one of them strays
I will search until I find it. I will
even give my life to save it.'

Come down, Zacchaeus!

This story tells what happened when Jesus met a cheating tax collector called Zacchaeus, and how Zacchaeus' life was changed.

It comes from Luke's Gospel, chapter 19.

'Jesus is coming to Jericho today!' The
news spread quickly, from house to
house, through the villages.

Everyone wanted to see him. They all
hoped Jesus would speak to them, or
that he would heal someone. They
wanted to hear him tell a story.

No one was going to do much work
today, because Jesus was coming.

One of the people who lived in Jericho was a man called Zacchaeus. No one liked Zacchaeus. His job was to collect the tax which each person had to pay.

He was not an honest man. Often he made people pay more than they were supposed to.

'That's why he's so rich and we're so poor,' said the people.

Zacchaeus heard the news that Jesus was coming.

The people said, 'Jesus says that money does not matter in God's kingdom. The poor will come first and many rich people will be left outside.'

Zacchaeus didn't like the sound of that, but he wanted to see Jesus.

Zacchaeus was a very short man. He could not see over the shoulders of the people who stood waiting in the village street.

The children had climbed up on top of the walls to see.

There wasn't room for Zacchaeus anywhere.

Then Zacchaeus had an idea. There were trees in the village street. He quickly ran to the nearest tree and pulled himself up to the lowest branches.

Some of the children saw him climb into the tree.

They called out, 'Hey, look at old Zacchaeus. He's climbing up that tree!' and they laughed as his short legs disappeared among the leaves.

Then everyone stopped thinking about Zacchaeus, or anyone else.

They passed the news down the street that Jesus was coming.

Everyone leaned forward to be the first
to see him. The children nearly toppled
off the wall. They hung onto each
other's arms.

They saw a group of people coming
down the street. But everyone knew at
once which man was Jesus. His face
made them smile and feel glad when
they saw him.

But why had Jesus stopped? Everyone was puzzled.

Jesus looked up into the tree. The people looked up too, and there was Zacchaeus peering down through the leaves.

'Zacchaeus,' Jesus called, laughing.
'Whatever are you doing up there?
Hurry and get down from that tree. I
want to spend today at your house.'

240

Zacchaeus was amazed as he scrambled down from the tree.

'How does Jesus know my name? How did he know I was there? He really seems to know me already.'

Zacchaeus kneeled down in the dusty road. The people couldn't believe what was happening.

'Please do come to my house,' they heard Zacchaeus say.

Zacchaeus hurried home to get things
ready. He sent his servants running to
do everything he told them. This was the
most important visitor he had ever had.

'We must offer him the best food we
have,' he told them.

But all the time Zacchaeus was thinking,
'Oh dear, Jesus is so good and he knows
all about me. I could see that. He'll
know about the money I've taken. He'll
know just what a bad man I am when
he sees this beautiful house.'

Jesus and his friends arrived, and they sat down to the meal. Zacchaeus felt worse and worse.

He saw the people going past the door.
They all peeped in and whispered,
'Look, Jesus is eating in the house of
Zacchaeus. Doesn't he know how
Zacchaeus gets his money?'

At last Zacchaeus could stand it no
longer.

He looked at Jesus and spoke to him.
Everyone stopped talking to listen to
him.

'Sir, you know everything already. You know what a wicked man I've been. But I want to put things right. I'm going to give away half my money to those poor people outside. And the money I stole from them I will pay back four times over.'

'Well done, Zacchaeus,' said Jesus, smiling at him. 'That's the way to show you've come into God's kingdom.

'I came to this world,' Jesus went on, 'to seek and to save lost people. I am glad I found you today, Zacchaeus.'

Mary, Martha and Lazarus

This story happened in a village called Bethany, near Jerusalem. Jesus showed that he was in charge of life and death by bringing his friend Lazarus back to life.

You can find the story in John's Gospel, chapter 11.

Mary and Martha were sisters. They
lived in a little house in Bethany, with
their brother Lazarus.

Jesus often came to visit them,
because they were his friends.

One day, in the house in Bethany, everyone was anxious. Lazarus was ill.

It wasn't the kind of illness where people tell you to 'go back to sleep and you'll feel better'. It was the kind where they knew that unless a miracle happened, Lazarus would die.

Mary and Martha had often seen Jesus work miracles. They had seen him make lame people walk and blind people see.

So they sent a message to Jesus to tell him how ill Lazarus was.

253

When Jesus was given the message, his friends were all with him. They knew how much Jesus loved the little family in Bethany. They expected Jesus to set off at once to see Lazarus.

But Jesus just carried on with what he was doing.

'We don't understand,' said one of the disciples to Jesus. 'The message said that Lazarus was so ill, he might die. Why don't you go to heal him?'

'There is a very good reason,' Jesus said. 'Wait and see.'

When they had waited for two days,
Jesus said, 'Now it is time to go to
Bethany.'

They said 'Goodbye' to the people
they had been staying with, and they set
off over the hills to Bethany.

As they walked along the street of the little village the people came out of their houses to talk to them.

They all knew Jesus.
'Why didn't you come?' they asked.
'Lazarus is dead.'

Then they all saw Martha, hurrying down the road towards them.

'Oh Jesus,' she cried. 'You loved him so much. I'm sure he would not have died if you had come before.'

Jesus told Martha, 'God will give Lazarus a new life if you believe what I say.'

'I know he will in the end, when we all see God,' Martha said, puzzled.

Jesus said, 'I am the resurrection and the life. Everyone who believes in me has that new life already, even though he dies. Don't be sad, Martha, just believe me.'

When Mary came out of the house, they
all went to the cave in the hillside where
Lazarus had been buried. The opening
of the cave had been closed with a huge
stone.

Everyone was crying. They were thinking how much they were going to miss Lazarus. Jesus cried with them.

Then he spoke in a loud voice that made them jump.

'Move that stone away from the cave,' he told them.

'But Lazarus has been dead for four days,' Martha protested.

The stone was pushed away. Jesus looked up and said to God, 'Father, thank you. I know you will do what I ask. And then all these people will believe that you sent me.'

Then Jesus looked at the dark entrance of the cave and shouted, 'Lazarus, come out!'

The people could hardly bear to look.
They were scared.

Mary and Martha trusted Jesus. They remembered Jesus had said that he was the resurrection and the life.

Suddenly, Lazarus was standing at the opening of the cave.

The people stood absolutely still, with their mouths wide open. They were amazed.

'Hurry up and untie the grave clothes he's wearing,' Jesus said.

One or two of the braver people did as Jesus said.

Then everyone crowded around Lazarus.
He looked completely well. His skin was
warm and his face was very happy.

Many of the people went back with
Jesus to the home of Lazarus, to
celebrate. Martha and Mary were so
glad that Jesus had come.

Some of the people went away to the
city. They told everyone they met about
what had happened.

'It was amazing,' they said. 'When
Jesus called him, Lazarus came out of
the cave, and now he is alive and well.'

But the priests and rulers were not
pleased. They were more jealous of Jesus
than ever before.

People Jesus met

This story tells of just some of the people whose lives were changed because they met Jesus.

You can find the story of Nicodemus in John's Gospel, chapter 3; the four friends in Mark, chapter 2; the woman at the well in John, chapter 4; the sick woman and Jairus' daughter in Luke, chapter 8; the ten 'lepers' in Luke, chapter 17; the rich young man in Matthew, chapter 19 and blind Bartimaeus in Mark, chapter 10.

The children in Galilee loved to be with Jesus.

'Let's go and find Jesus,' they said.

Their parents often left the work they were doing in their homes or fields and went with them to see Jesus.

Jesus was never too busy to talk to people.

The crowds enjoyed watching Jesus heal the sick people. Sometimes a man walked for the very first time, or a person who had been blind pointed at the trees and flowers he could suddenly see.

The people listened when Jesus answered difficult questions and explained about God's kingdom.

Do you remember the man called
Nicodemus? He was an important man
who had a lot of questions to ask Jesus.
He was worried in case other leaders
saw him going to Jesus.

So Nicodemus waited until night-
time.

'You must believe me, Nicodemus,' said Jesus firmly. 'God loved the world so much that he sent me, his own Son, to give eternal life to everyone who believes in me.'

Nicodemus went away with a lot to think about.

He never forgot the day he met Jesus.

There was a man who had never
walked because his legs did not work
properly. So his four friends took him
to see Jesus.

They almost gave up when they saw
the crowds.

Then one of them had a good idea.

'Let's put him down through that hole in the roof,' he said.

Jesus healed the man, and he even helped his friends carry his own bed home. That man never forgot the day he met Jesus.

Do you remember the woman from Samaria who met Jesus at the well? She was surprised when he offered her a·drink of water.

'You have no bucket to dip into the well,' she said.

'The water I can give you is God's water of eternal life. In God's kingdom no one need ever be thirsty again.'

The woman went back to the town.

'Jesus must be God's Son,' she told the people. 'He knew all about me.'

And she never forgot the day she met Jesus.

Some people were very shy about
asking Jesus for help.

One woman needed Jesus to heal her.
She had been ill for a long time. She
spent all her money to see the doctors
but none of them could make her better.

The woman watched Jesus healing the sick people.

'Even if I could touch his coat I would be well,' she thought.

So she reached out to touch the coat of Jesus as he went by. She was better! Jesus had healed her.

She never forgot the day she met Jesus.

Jairus ran to fetch Jesus. His little girl was dying and no one could make her better.

But there were so many people around Jesus that by the time they arrived at the house, the little girl had died.

Everyone in the house was crying. Jesus went into the little girl's room and took her hand.

'Get up now,' he said. Everyone was amazed when she got up alive and well.

Jairus never forgot the day he met Jesus.

One day Jesus heard some men calling out to him, 'Jesus, look at the mess we are in.'

They had a terrible illness. Their skin was horrid. Nobody wanted to go near them.

Jesus looked at their hands and faces.

'Now you have called out my name you'll be well,' Jesus told them. 'Go home.'

On the way home they saw that their skin was smooth. The sores had gone. They were in such a hurry to show their families that they forgot to say 'Thank you'.

Only one man came back to thank Jesus for making him better.

He never forgot the day he met Jesus.

An important man came to Jesus.

'You keep telling us about the life of God's kingdom,' he said. 'I want to know more about it. How can I have this life?'

Everyone waited to hear what Jesus would say. They all wanted to know that answer.

'You love God and do as he says–but I think you love your money more than you love God,' said Jesus. 'If you gave it all away you would be ready to have God's life.'

The man went away very sad. He couldn't bear to give away his money because he was very rich.

That man never forgot the day he met Jesus.

Blind Bartimaeus sat by the side of the road to Jericho. Everyone knew him.

When he heard Jesus coming he shouted loudly, 'Jesus, listen to me.'

The people all said, 'Be quiet,' but he shouted all the more loudly.

Jesus stopped.

'What do you want me to do?' he asked.

'If only I could see,' said the blind man.

'You shall,' said Jesus, 'because you believed in me.'

Suddenly Bartimaeus could see how beautiful the world was.

He never forgot the day he met Jesus.

Everyone who met Jesus went away to tell other people about him.

None of them ever forgot the day they met Jesus.

Jesus the King

Long before Jesus was born, God had promised his people a king who would bring them peace. On his last visit to Jerusalem, Jesus was given a king's welcome.

You can find the story in Matthew's Gospel, chapter 21.

'Jesus is coming, Jesus is coming,'
the people said to each other in
Jerusalem.

The city was full of people, ready for
the Passover Festival.

Crowds of people rushed out to the
main road. They waited for a long time
and at last they saw him coming,
riding on a donkey.

The people pulled off their cloaks and
spread them on the road for the donkey
to walk on.

Then they pulled branches down
from the trees and waved them as Jesus
rode by.

'Hurrah! God bless the king who comes in the name of the Lord!' they shouted. 'Praise God's name!'

The crowd was pleased to see Jesus come to Jerusalem. Many years ago the prophets had written that their king would ride into Jerusalem on a donkey Now, here he was!

In Jerusalem Jesus went to God's temple with all the other people.

In the courtyard there was a market. There was a lot of noise.

When Jesus saw the money-changers cheating people he was really angry.

'God's temple is meant to be a house for prayer but you have made it like a hide-out for thieves. Get out!' Jesus shouted.

He ran through the market, pushing over the tables and spilling all the money.

There were many blind beggars and
lame people at the entrance to the
temple. They came to Jesus and he
made them well.

For the first time in their lives, the blind
people could see the temple and the
lame people could jump about.

The children cheered and shouted.

Many of the priests in the temple
had decided that Jesus was dangerous
because the people listened to him.
They were trying to find a way to kill
him.

'We have waited long enough,' they
all agreed. 'It's time to get rid of Jesus.'

But God had already told his Son what his plans were. Jesus knew he had to be in Jerusalem, even though the men were planning to kill him.

A few days later Jesus asked his
disciples to prepare the special Passover
meal so that they could eat together.
Jesus was sad because he knew
it was the last time he would have
a meal with his disciples.

In the evening Jesus and his disciples
met together in an upstairs room.
Everything was ready for the meal.

The disciples' feet were dusty from the long day. Jesus took off his cloak and knelt down to wash their feet. He dried them with a towel.

The disciples said, 'This can't be right. You are our master. You shouldn't be doing the servant's work.'

'It is the servant's work,' said Jesus. 'I wanted to show you that my followers must learn to serve each other.'

They sat down to the special meal.

When they were eating Jesus said,
'One of you is going to help my
enemies catch me.'

They were so horrified by what Jesus had said that they did not notice Judas going out of the room. He was going to tell the priests how they could catch Jesus.

Then Jesus took some bread.

He said thank you to God, then he broke the bread in pieces so that there was some on each plate.

'Eat this now,' he said. 'Soon my body will be broken for you just like this bread.'

Then Jesus took a cup of wine.

He said thank you to God, then he passed it around and they all drank from it.

'Drink this now,' he said. 'I am going to die and my blood will be poured out for you, like this wine.'

After the meal Jesus and the disciples went for a walk.

Jesus said, 'All of you are going to run away and leave me.'

The disciples were all upset and Simon Peter said, 'I don't care what anyone else does. I will never let you down.'

Jesus said, 'But you will, Simon Peter.
You'll even say that you don't know me.'
Simon Peter said, 'I'll never do that!'
And so did all the other disciples

Then they went to one of the places
they loved best–the garden of olive trees
at Gethsemane.

Jesus went away on his own to pray,
to talk to God his Father.

All the disciples felt sad. They
did not understand. They were afraid.

A few days before, the people had shouted, 'God bless the king who comes in the name of the Lord.' Now Jesus was saying he had to die.

The disciples did not know that Jesus was a very special king of a very special kingdom.

What was going to happen next?

Jesus on trial

No sooner had Jesus been welcomed as king than he was arrested. He was accused of crimes he never committed, and killed by being fixed with nails onto a cross of wood.

This is the story of the first Good Friday. It comes near the end of all four Gospels—Matthew, Mark, Luke and John.

Jesus and the disciples were in
Jerusalem. They had eaten the special
Passover meal together. Then they had
walked slowly out of the city, up the
steep road to the orchard of olive-trees,
called the Garden of Gethsemane.

'Stay here,' Jesus said, 'while I talk to God my Father. Pray for me. This is the most difficult hour of my life.'

Jesus went and knelt down on the ground.

'Please save me from all this pain and agony,' he called out to God. 'How can I bear it? But if I must die, so that you can bring people into your kingdom, I am willing to die.'

When he came back to the disciples,
they were fast asleep. Jesus woke them
up.

'Couldn't you stay awake, just for me?'
he asked.

'Look,' Jesus said. 'There are people coming to arrest me.'

They could see the soldiers coming through the trees, with lights and swords.

The disciples began to feel afraid.

Then they saw that the man leading the
soldiers was one of the disciples — their
friend Judas. But he did not look at
them.

The priests had paid Judas a lot of
money to help them catch Jesus. Judas
went up to Jesus and kissed him, to
show the soldiers which man to arrest.

The crowd of soldiers gathered around Jesus, with swords drawn.

'You don't need those swords,' Jesus said. 'Didn't you notice me in the temple today? Why didn't you arrest me then?'

The disciples were so afraid that they all ran away into the darkness of the garden.

When the soldiers had taken Jesus away, the disciples went back to the little room where they had eaten supper together. Only Simon Peter turned back. He crept along behind the soldiers, to see where they took Jesus.

Jesus was taken to the house of the chief priest. The priests had decided to arrest and question Jesus at night. In the daytime he was always with crowds of people.

Jesus had not done anything wrong, so
the priests had to pay people to come
and tell lies about him.

Simon Peter followed the soldiers. But when they took Jesus away to question him, Simon Peter waited outside with some of the servants. He came closer to the fire, to keep warm.

Simon Peter heard the chief priest say to Jesus, 'Is it true that you are God's Son — the one he promised to send?'

'I am,' Jesus answered.

'Now we've heard your lies for ourselves,' they shouted. 'We will have you killed, because you have pretended to be God's Son.'

Outside in the dark, a servant girl came up to the fire and looked at Simon Peter. The firelight flickered on his face as he held his hands close to the burning logs.

'Aren't you one of the disciples of Jesus?' she said.

Simon Peter was frightened.

'No, of course I'm not,' he said quickly. 'I've never even met him.' Three times he said the same thing.

Then it was dawn, and a cock crowed.
As Jesus was led away, he looked at
Simon Peter.

'I promised tonight that I would
always be his friend,' Simon Peter
thought. 'And now I've said I don't even
know him.'

Then Simon Peter ran away, crying.

The soldiers then took Jesus to Pilate, the Emperor's ruler in Jerusalem.

'Are you trying to become a king?' Pilate asked Jesus. The Emperor would not like that!

'My kingdom does not belong to this world,' Jesus said. 'You say that I am a king. But I came into this world only to tell people about God's truth.'

'Well then, I don't know what all this trouble is about,' said Pilate. He went outside to the priests.

'I can't find anything this man has done wrong,' said Pilate.

'He pretends to be God's Son. By our law he must die,' shouted the priests.

'What has he done?' asked Pilate. But
they just shouted, 'Crucify him! Crucify
him!'

Pilate was tired of arguing. He was
afraid there would be a riot. The
Emperor would not like that. So he
agreed that Jesus should be crucified.

The priests were very pleased. They
were going to get rid of Jesus at last.

All the people who loved Jesus
watched sadly, as he carried the wooden
cross up the hill, out of the city. They
had wanted Jesus to be their king.

Jesus knew he was finishing the work
God had given him to do.

Jesus looked down from the cross. He saw his disciples and his mother, Mary.

He knew that when he died they would be very sad.

So he said to John, one of his special friends, 'Look after my mother for me, John, as if you were her son.'

'Forgive these people, Father,' he said to God. 'They don't know what they are doing.'

Then Jesus died.

'He really was the Son of God,' said one of the soldiers standing guard.

The disciples were very sad. They thought that everything was over. They would never see Jesus again. But they were wrong!

The first Easter

You have read how Jesus was killed. It seemed like the end of the world to his friends. But it was not the end of the story. The saddest day was to be followed by the happiest day of their lives.

What happened next is told at the end of all four Gospels—Matthew, Mark, Luke and John.

After Jesus had been crucified, Joseph
and Nicodemus, two of his friends,
wrapped up his body and buried it in a
garden cave. They rolled a great stone
across the opening. Soldiers stood guard
in case of trouble.

The disciples, and some of the others
who had loved Jesus, went back to the
room where they had had the special
supper. They felt scared and very sad.

But very early on Sunday morning some of the women took oils and spices to put on the body of Jesus. They went out into the dark, silent streets. They knew that Jesus' body had been put into a cave. But there had not been time to do things properly.

The women went quietly into the garden.

They wondered how they would get into the cave. But as they came near, they gasped with surprise. The enormous stone had been rolled away from the opening and the guards had gone.

The women ran and peered into the
cave. It was empty! Whatever had
happened? They began to feel worried.

At that moment they saw two men, in
bright, shining clothes, standing beside
the cave. The women could hardly
believe their eyes.

'Why are you looking for Jesus here?' the angels asked. 'He is alive! Don't you remember how he told you that he would be killed but would come back to life again? Run and tell the disciples.'

The women ran back through the city streets, as fast as they could go.

'Jesus is alive — the angels of God have spoken to us,' they gasped to each other as they ran.

When the women arrived at the room where the others were, they banged on the door as hard as they could.

'Open the door,' they called to the disciples. 'We have the best news you've ever heard. Jesus is alive!'

That same day, two of Jesus' friends were walking home to Emmaus. They did not know that Jesus was alive.

'There's no reason to stay in Jerusalem now that Jesus is dead,' they said. 'We're going home.'

As they walked down the road, another man caught up with them. He did not seem to know what had been happening, so they told him about Jesus' death.

To their surprise, the man began to explain to them why Jesus had to die.

'Come in and have some supper,' they said to him, when they reached home.

At the supper table the visitor took the bread, thanked God for it and began to share it around. Then, at last, they knew who he was. It had been Jesus all the time!

But as soon as they recognized him, he disappeared.

'We must go back to Jerusalem at once and tell the others,' they said.

Although it was night-time they hurried back to Jerusalem.

When the two friends arrived, they heard what had happened when the women went to the cave.

'We didn't believe them,' said Simon Peter and John, 'but when we went to the garden we found that it was true. Jesus really is alive.'

While the disciples were talking together, Jesus himself came into the room. They all gasped and backed away.

'It's all right,' Jesus said. 'I'm not a ghost, and I would like something to eat.'

The disciples watched him eat some supper. It was wonderful to see Jesus again.

But one disciple was missing. Thomas
had not been there to see Jesus.

When they all told him that Jesus was
alive, Thomas said, 'I will not believe it
until I see him with my own eyes and
touch the place where the nails went.'

The very next Sunday, they were all together and Thomas was with them. Jesus came again.

'Here I am, Thomas,' he said quietly. 'Reach out and touch me. Now will you believe that I really am alive?'

'I do believe,' said Thomas. 'You are my Lord and my God.

After this, Jesus' friends went home to Lake Galilee. One morning they were out fishing in their boat. They had fished all night, but still the nets were empty.

Suddenly a man called out from the beach, 'Let down the nets on the other side of the boat.'

'Does he think we don't know how to fish?' they said. But they did as they were told. Soon the nets were bulging with enormous fish.

'It's Jesus!' they all shouted.

That morning, as they had breakfast together, Jesus had a quiet word with Peter. He was forgiven for that dreadful morning when he had said he did not know Jesus. And he was told he had special work to do.

Six weeks went by, and Jesus took his disciples for a walk up the hill outside Jerusalem.

'You have seen how God gave me power to heal sick people and give life to those who were dead,' Jesus said. 'You have heard all about God's kingdom.'

'Now it's time for me to go back to my
Father. I want you to tell everyone about
me.

'Go to Jerusalem and wait there. For
God will give you the same power that
he gave me.'

Then the clouds came down, and
when they cleared, Jesus had gone.

The disciples went back to Jerusalem,
and waited.

They prayed to God, as Jesus had
taught them. They talked of all the
wonderful things they had seen and
heard while they had been with Jesus.

They did not know it, but an exciting
new life was about to begin.

Good news
for everyone

This is the story of what happened to the disciples after Jesus had left them and gone back to be with God.

You can find it in the book of Acts, chapters 1 to 4.

Jesus had gone back to heaven to be with God. But his disciples had important work to do. They were to tell the whole world about Jesus!

'You will need God's special help,' Jesus said. 'So go back to Jerusalem and wait there.'

One day, when the disciples were all
together, praying, there was a sudden
noise, as if a gale of wind was rushing
through the house.

Then they saw what looked like
tongues of fire that reached out and
touched each one of them. They looked
at each other in amazement.

They began to speak, and found
themselves talking in languages they did
not even know. They felt very excited
and full of joy.

'God has sent the special help that
Jesus promised us,' they shouted. They
made so much noise that a big crowd
gathered.

The disciples forgot how frightened they had been. Now they wanted to tell the whole world about Jesus and God's kingdom.

Jerusalem was full of visitors from other countries, because it was the festival of Pentecost.

The disciples rushed outside and started to tell the crowd the wonderful story of Jesus.

Everyone could understand. Each of the visitors heard them speaking in his own language!

It was a miracle. God had given the disciples the special help they needed to tell the people about the kingdom of God. They could not see Jesus any more, but God had sent his Holy Spirit to live in each of them, always.

The most amazing person to watch was
Simon Peter. When Jesus had died,
Simon Peter had been very frightened.
All he had wanted was to go back to
being a fisherman on Lake Galilee.

But now Simon Peter was filled with God's power. He stood up in front of everyone and explained the good news of God's kingdom. His face was shining with joy and gladness.

A few days later, Simon Peter and
another disciple, John, went to the
temple to worship God. They were full of
praise.

They wanted to thank God for the
special help he had given them.

As they went through the gate, they saw
a man who had never been able to walk,
sitting there asking for money.

Every day his friends brought him to
the gate, so that he could beg from the
people who were going to the temple.

'Please give me some money,' he called out to Simon Peter and John.

'We don't have any money,' said Simon Peter. 'But we do have something to give you. In the name of Jesus, I tell you to stand up and walk!'

Simon Peter took him by the hand, and the man stood up. His feet and legs became strong. He started to leap and jump about.

He went with them into the temple, shouting praises to God at the top of his voice.

When the people in the temple saw him,
they stopped what they were doing.

'Just a minute,' they said, 'aren't you
the man who sat at the temple gate?
What's happened to you?'

The man told them.

Simon Peter said, 'I don't know why you are so surprised. We didn't do this by ourselves. Jesus from Nazareth, whom you killed, was God's own Son. God raised him to life again. Now he has gone back to be with God, but God has given us his special power.

'Tell God you are sorry for what you did and he will forgive you. Believe us, Jesus is alive.'

Many people were excited to hear that
Jesus was still alive, especially the
people who had been healed by him, or
had enjoyed listening to his teaching.

In the city of Jerusalem many people believed the good news of God's kingdom, and God gave them the special power he had given to Jesus.

Day after day, more and more people found that what the disciples were so joyful about was really true. Jesus was still alive!

The priests and leaders in Jerusalem were horrified to find that the disciples of Jesus were telling everyone that he was alive again.

'Stop telling the people about Jesus,' they told Simon Peter and John.

'We can't,' the disciples said. 'Jesus told us to tell the whole world.'

They told everyone they met about Jesus.

More and more people became followers
of Jesus. They often met together in the
temple, to thank God for his kingdom
and his help.

They often had meals together in each
others' homes. If anyone was poor, or
had no food, the others shared their food
or money with them.

They really loved each other. And they knew it was because God was giving them his special help.

He had made them into new people, by giving them his own Holy Spirit. They were completely changed.

The priests and leaders in Jerusalem
made up their minds to stop people
talking about God's kingdom. The
followers of Jesus were punished. They
had to leave the city and go to other
towns and villages.

But this was the best thing that could have happened.

It meant that the good news about God's kingdom was now being told to the whole world.

Paul at Damascus

When Jesus had gone back to be with God, the disciples were given the work of telling the whole world about Jesus and God's kingdom. Paul, an important man in Jerusalem, was one of those who tried to stop them.

You can find this story in the book of Acts, chapter 9.

Paul was a leader in Jerusalem.
Everyone knew him. He was very clever
and he served God. Many people came
to him for advice, because he knew so
much about God's Law.

Paul had heard a lot about the disciples of Jesus Christ. They had been very afraid when Jesus had been killed. They just hid away together in a little room.

But now they had changed, and they seemed to be everywhere. They worshipped in the temple, they preached on the street corners.

There was even news of people being healed by the disciples in the name of Jesus.

Paul did not believe that Jesus really was God's Son. He did not know that God had given the disciples the special help of his Holy Spirit. Paul thought they were just making trouble.

So he set out with his friends to stop them.

Paul went from house to house. When he
found people who talked about Jesus and
the kingdom of God, he dragged them
out of their homes and took them off to
prison. Some of them died.

The priests and leaders in Jerusalem
thought he was doing a splendid job.

One day, Paul set out from Jerusalem to the city of Damascus. He had heard that some of Jesus' followers were there.

But, as he was going along the road, a blinding light suddenly shone down on him. It made his eyes hurt so much that he could not see.

Then a voice called to him. He could hear it clearly.

'Paul!' shouted the voice. 'Paul!'

'Who are you?' asked Paul. 'I can't see anything with this blazing light. Tell me who you are.'

'My name is Jesus,' was the answer. 'I am the one you are fighting against. You are wrong, Paul. I am alive. Get up now, and go into Damascus. Wait there until you are told what to do.'

Paul was amazed. He could not argue with the voice. He could not see the bright light any more. Everything was dark. Paul, the strong leader, was blind and helpless.

The friends who were with Paul had heard the voice but they could not see anyone there.

They helped Paul get up from the ground. They led him by the hand, as he stumbled into Damascus.

No one was afraid of Paul when he arrived in Damascus. For three days he just sat in the house.

He could not see anything. He did not want to eat or drink.

All he could think about was what had happened on the way.

Paul did not know that God was sending
someone to help him.

The man's name was Ananias and he
belonged to God's kingdom. He had
heard about Paul and the terrible things
he had done. He knew why Paul had
come to Damascus.

God spoke to Ananias.

'Ananias,' he said. 'I have something I want you to do for me today.'

'I want you to visit a man called Paul, who is staying in Damascus,' God said.

'But I can't do that,' gasped Ananias. 'He is our worst enemy. He has come to Damascus to take your people back to prison in Jerusalem.'

God told Ananias
what had happened to
Paul on his way to Damascus.

'I have told him that you are going to come and make him see again,' God said.

Poor Ananias! He was so afraid.

'Don't worry,' God said to Ananias.
'I have chosen Paul for very special
work. I am going to change him, just as
I have changed you. He will tell many
nations about me, although that will not
be an easy job for him.'

So Ananias made his way through the
streets of Damascus to the house where
Paul was staying. Ananias trusted in
God and he knew God had given him
the special power that Jesus had.

But he did wonder what was going to
happen next.

Ananias knocked at the door and went into the house where Paul was. He put his hands on Paul's shoulders.

'Brother Paul,' he said, 'God has sent me so that you can see again and receive the gift of his Holy Spirit.'

At once Paul could see again. He knew now that Jesus was the Son of God. Everything Jesus' followers said about him was true. Paul no longer wanted to punish them. Instead he wanted to help them tell the whole world the good news about Jesus.

The people in Damascus could not
believe their eyes when they saw the
way Paul had changed.

'We thought Paul had come to take us
off to prison,' they said. 'But now he
can't stop talking about Jesus.'

Paul's old friends could not think what had come over him.

'How can Paul be a follower of Jesus,' they said. 'We can't believe it.'

But it was true. God had chosen Paul, the man who had done so much harm, to take the good news of Jesus to people of many nations.

Paul and friends

This story is about some of the adventures of a man called Paul. He had been one of those who tried to stop the followers of Jesus telling others about him. Paul put many of Jesus' followers into prison.

But then he saw Jesus for himself and became his most loyal follower.

These stories come from the book of Acts: the Damascus story from chapter 9; the Antioch story from chapters 11 and 13; Lystra from chapter 14; the Jerusalem Council from chapter 15 and Philippi from chapter 16.

When Paul set out for the city of Damascus, he wanted to arrest anyone who talked about Jesus and to throw them into prison.

But, on the way to Damascus, God stopped him and spoke to him.

Paul ended up by wanting to talk about Jesus himself!

The followers of Jesus in Damascus were very excited.

'Paul is one of us now,' they said. 'He will want to preach about Jesus, instead of throwing us into prison.'

'How can Paul change his mind like that?' Paul's old friends asked each other. 'We must kill him before he starts spreading this story about Jesus coming to life again.'

But the followers of Jesus heard of their plan, and one night they helped Paul to escape from Damascus. They let him down from the city wall in a basket!

In the city of Antioch, followers of Jesus were sharing the good news. The people there were excited.

'We need to be different,' some of them said. 'Can God make us into new people, too?'

So many believed and turned to God, that the people in Antioch began to call the followers of Jesus Christ by a new name. They called them Christians.

News from Antioch reached Jerusalem. A man called Barnabas went to help, and he asked Paul to join him.

They saw that, when people believed in Jesus, God gave each of them a job to do. He gave some of them special power to heal sick people. Some found that they were able to preach. Others had the special job of helping people.

Everyone knew that God had given Paul and Barnabas a very special job. The people of Antioch could not keep them there. They must travel to other towns and cities with the good news of Jesus.

When Paul and Barnabas arrived at
Lystra, they started to tell people in the
street the good news about Jesus.

One person who listened to every
word was a poor, crippled man, who
had never been able to walk.

The man believed all that Paul said. Paul knew that God would heal him.

'Stand up,' Paul said.

The man jumped up. He started walking around. His legs became strong and healthy.

When the crowds saw what had
happened, they thought that Paul and
Barnabas had done this by themselves.
  'They must be gods, pretending to be
men,' the people shouted.

'Don't be silly,' Paul said. 'We are just ordinary people, like you. We have come to bring good news from the God who made our world. It is his power that made the lame man walk. You must believe in him.'

After many long journeys, Paul and
Barnabas went to Jerusalem. There the
leaders were waiting to talk to them.
They had an important meeting.

'First of all, we thought that God's good news was just for his special people, the Jews,' said Simon Peter. 'But now we wonder if God wants everyone to hear about it. What do you think, Paul?'

So Paul and Barnabas stood up and told of the adventures they had had. They told them about the people who had been healed and the people God had changed by giving them his Holy Spirit.

'God is doing all this for people everywhere,' said Paul, 'not just for his special people, the Jews. So we know his plan is for the whole world to hear the good news.'

All the apostles and leaders agreed with him.

So Paul set off again with the good
news. This time he took a friend called
Silas. They went by land and sea, until
they came to the city of Philippi.

As soon as they arrived, they went to
a place on the river bank where people
met to pray. Paul told them about Jesus,
and the good news that they could be
forgiven and start a new life.

Many people in Philippi believed what
Paul and Silas were teaching. But others
made trouble. Paul and Silas were
marched off to prison.

The two men were whipped and
locked up for the night.

Paul and Silas sat in the dirty, smelly
prison. It was very late and their backs
hurt badly, where they had been
whipped. But they began to pray and to
sing songs of praise to God. They sang
about his love and power. They sang
about Jesus and how he had risen to life
again.

While they were singing, the ground shook and the prison walls trembled. It was an earthquake!

The locks on the doors were shaken loose. The prisoners were free!

The prison guard came running in. If
the prisoners escaped, he would be
killed.

But, to his amazement, Paul called
out, 'We are all here.'

'This is the work of your God,' the
guard said. 'He has set you free. I want
him to forgive me and to be my God too.'

So the prison guard and all his family
believed in God and became followers of
Jesus.

Paul journeyed on. He knew there were so many people who had never even heard of Jesus.

He wanted to use every moment, telling them God's good news.

Paul the prisoner

Rome was the most important city in the world at the time of Jesus, and of his special follower, Paul. The emperor of Rome ruled the world.

Paul knew that he must take the good news about Jesus to Rome before he died.

You can find the story of how that happened in the book of Acts, starting at chapter 25.

The followers of Jesus in Jerusalem were
very worried.

Paul, their friend, who went
everywhere telling people the good news
about Jesus, had been arrested.

His enemies had made trouble, and
now he was in prison, in a place called
Caesarea.

But that did not stop Paul telling people about Jesus.

He talked to the guards. He talked at his trial. He talked to the governor and even to the king.

'I have done nothing wrong,' Paul said. 'I have only told people that Jesus, who was killed, is alive again.'

'It is a matter for your own people to decide,' said the governor. 'You will have to go to Jerusalem.'

'Although I am a Jew, I am also a citizen of Rome,' Paul told them. 'I claim my right to be judged by the emperor.'

'Then we shall send you to Rome,' the governor said.

Paul and some other prisoners were led on to a boat which was sailing for Rome.

Paul was glad to have his friend Luke with him. There was a soldier in charge of them.

When the boat had been sailing for some time a terrible storm started.

The wind howled around the boat. It
blew the waves high, over the decks. The
boat was tossed up and down on the
sea.

The prisoners were afraid. So were the
sailors.

'We'll all be drowned,' they screamed.

But Paul knew that they were not going to be drowned. God had told him that they would all arrive safely. He shouted to the men to trust God.

At last, when daylight came, they saw an island nearby.

But suddenly there was a terrible crash. The boat had been thrown onto a sandbank. It was hit by giant waves and began to break in pieces.

Clinging to planks torn from the boat, they all jumped into the cold sea and struggled to the island.

They helped each other out of the water and stumbled up the beach. Their clothes were wet and cold. The wind blew the sand into their faces.

Quickly they collected wood for a fire. Some people from the island helped them. They began to dry themselves by the fire.

Paul reached out to put more sticks on the fire. He did not see that there was a snake in the sticks. The people gasped when they saw the snake bite him. They thought he would die.

But Paul just shook the snake off. Nothing happened to him. They knew, then, that God was keeping him safe.

When winter was over, it was time to set sail again for Rome. They went on board another boat.

This time the weather and the winds were just right and they arrived safely.

There were people in Rome who already knew about Jesus. When they heard that Paul was coming, they went down the road to meet him.

Paul was so pleased to find that he already had friends in Rome who followed Jesus.

The soldier in charge of the prisoners took Paul to a house.

'You have not hurt anyone, or stolen anything,' he said, 'so you can stay in this house. You will have a soldier to guard you, and you are not allowed to go out. But your friends can visit you.'

So the people who wanted to hear about
Jesus came to see Paul in his house. Paul
enjoyed telling them all about Jesus and
the kingdom of God.

Paul spent much of his time writing letters. He had preached in many towns, so he had lots of friends. They would be wondering where he was.

Some of his friends had heard only a little about Jesus and God's kingdom. Paul wrote long letters to them.

He told them what was happening to him. He reminded them about how Jesus had died for them and risen to life again. God had given them new lives. Paul was excited as he thought about how different they were now.

Paul chose some of his trusted friends to take the letters. They had to travel by boat and by donkey.

Sometimes they had to walk a long way to reach the people Paul had written to.

When a letter arrived, all the Christians met together to read it over and over again. They wanted to learn all they could about living in God's kingdom.

The Christians took great care of Paul's letters, and we can still read many of them in our Bible. There is even a letter Paul wrote to the people in Rome before he arrived there.

There are letters to people in Corinth, Thessalonica, Galatia, Ephesus, Philippi and Colossae.

And there are letters Paul wrote to special friends — to Timothy, Titus and Philemon.

Paul followed Jesus all his life and
looked forward to going to be with him
when he died. They say that Paul was
killed in Rome because he preached the
good news about Jesus Christ.

That same good news has been passed on to people all over the world for two thousand years.

We are still talking about it today.

God's great plan was to rescue and renew his spoiled world. It began with Abraham and the nation he founded. It was completed in the life and work of God's own Son, Jesus Christ, through his death and his coming alive again.

From that day to this, the work of Jesus' followers has been to share the good news with people everywhere. God gives new life to everyone who comes to him. And so the story goes on . . .